Jamie and the
Race Brace

A story to empower kids living with Cerebral Palsy

Dear Reader,

Imagine that your brain is an ocean, and in that ocean there are many little islands. Each island controls a different part of your body. The islands are connected by bridges so that information can travel smoothly between the brain and your body, but sometimes one or more of these bridges can be damaged. When a bridge is damaged, some parts of your body might not work properly (which may look a little funny at first) or they might not work at all.

This is what happens to someone with Cerebral Palsy (CP) and it is the most common motor disability in children.

CP kids might walk a little awkwardly and they might need braces or a wheelchair. They will need to see doctors and specialists and do a lot of physical therapy. Having CP can be painful and annoying and there are many other challenges to overcome, but with the help of your medical team, braces, exercise and family support you will be able to reach goals that you never thought possible.

So try your best and go for it!

Luna (11 years)
- born with Cerebral Palsy -

ISBN: 979-8-666-28117-8

Jamie and the
Race Brace

A *Jamie* Book

children's books for

Optimists!

words and pictures by Jana D. Wingels

Today is the first day of Fall.
My brother Tom, his Special Leg
and I walk home from school,
when suddenly…

…we meet an interesting Flyer.

*"Fun Race!
Be part of the Big Race!
October 1st at 9 am.
Take a while and run a mile.
No registration needed.
Age 1 - 99"*, says the Flyer.

Tom is very excited.
"We will take part in that race," he
says to his leg. *"And we will win!"*

"Let me be your coach!"
I reply, knowing Tom and his Special
Leg will need my support.

We drop off our school bags at home…

… and head off to the track for our first practice.

"Ready - Set - GO!"
I shout and hit the button
on my stopwatch.

Tom rushes
forward...

… but as soon as his toes hit the track his Special Leg flings backwards and lands on the ground. *"Sorry."* it says *"But you knew I was special*!"*

* Tom's Special Leg has Cerebral Palsy (CP), so Tom cannot always control the way his leg moves. Typically a patient with CP walks on tippy toes with bended knees. But don't worry, CP patients will not actually lose a leg when they run.

"We'll figure this out," I tell my brother and his leg while putting them back together.

"Hmm, maybe some tape will help us stick together," suggests Tom's Special Leg. So I tape his leg back on.

"Let's try again," says
my brother and his leg.
"Ready - Set - GO!" I shout.

They run forward…

.. but the Special Leg falls off again.
"Ouch!" shouts Tom.

Tape might not be enough,
so I drag out something
that might hold a little better.

"How about we staple you together? That way you will HAVE to follow one another!" I suggest.

"Go for it, coach!" Tom and his Special Leg reply half bravely.

* *Warning: NEVER try to staple your siblings.*

"Now we can get back to practice!"
Tom and his leg say.
"Ready - Set - GO!" I shout again.

But as they lunge forward…

… the staples hold-
ing his Special leg
snap off. His leg flies
up and hits the Flyer.

"There is no hope for us running together," Tom mutters while hopping over on one leg.

My brother is really upset. His Special Leg is very sad. But I am all out of ideas.

Tom and his Special Leg want
to give up racing all together.
That means I will lose my job
as a coach.
I wish we could find a solution.

As we slowly make our way back home…

…a cheerful door suddenly appears in front of us.

"Do your legs need fixing?" asks the door.
"Then the Leg Lab is your place!" he says joyfully and invites us in.

"Let's go inside and get inspired!" I say excitedly.

The friendly door opens
with a smile. I push Tom and
his Special Leg inside.

"Looks like we found the right place for me!" says the Special Leg as it hops into the lab.

We find all kinds of materials for making casting molds, foot braces or even brand new legs.

"Are you going to replace me?" asks the leg a bit worried.

*"Of course not!" I reply.
"But let's create a support for you, so you will be able to run as fast as Tom!"
"I'm in!" replies Tom.
"I'm in too!"
says Tom's leg.*

First, I create a cast mold
of Tom's Special Leg.

"Give me a moment," I tell Tom and his leg. *"It's time for me to become an orthotist* and create a race brace."*

* An orthotist can make shoe inserts, orthoses (leg braces) and protheses (leg replacements) to help a patient walk better.

I am so proud to present my brother and his Special Leg with their new *RACE BRACE!*

But before we try it on, I join
my brother and his Special Leg
for their stretching.

After their exercise Tom and his Special Leg try on their new brace.

"It fits!" says the leg delighted. *"Now you are ready to reach out for your goal."* I say as I add a finishing touch to the new *Race Brace*.

On Race Day we gather
along the track.

I am confident.
Mom is excited.
Dad is cheering.
Even the Leg Lab is here to support us.
Tom and his Special Leg are ready to go.

"Ready - Set - GO!"
the announcer shouts.

Tom runs forward, …

… his heel hits the
track and both legs
work together.

My brother rushes
along the track…

…and finally finishes
that Big Race!

We are proud of Tom.
Tom is proud of his leg.
"I told you I'm special," says
his leg while showing off its
new Race Brace.

And in my mind I am already
preparing for the next big race.

Jana Dietsch Wingels combined her skills as a children's book author and an optimistic mother of a daughter with Cerebral Palsy (CP). Jana knows about the challenges that CP kids face every day: staying motivated throughout medical appointments, doing Physical Therapy, wearing ortheses, and many more. Jana's book *Jamie and the Race Brace* aims to empower CP kids and their families with a positive message about overcoming obstacles. Let's see every little achievement as a big success!

Want to read more of Jamie's adventures?

Jamie and the Big Move
A story to empower kids coping with change

Jamie goes green
A story to empower kids making Earth friendly choices

Made in the USA
Las Vegas, NV
03 May 2024

89439759R10026